SUPER SUB

SUPER SUB

ALAN GIBBONS

With illustrations by
David Shephard

Barrington Stoke

First published in 2022 in Great Britain by
Barrington Stoke Ltd
18 Walker Street, Edinburgh, EH3 7LP

www.barringtonstoke.co.uk

A CIP catalogue record for this book is available
from the British Library upon request

ISBN: 978-1-80090-062-2

Printed by Hussar Books, Poland

Contents

Chapter 1
Bengo

I had only been part of my new football team for four weeks when I met Bengo. My family had just moved up north from Stoke. Football was how I made new friends, but I'd never met Bengo. He hadn't been at training and so I didn't know anything about him.

Bengo was short and skinny. He looked as if the wind could blow him over. He showed up on the day of a match and everybody crowded round him. They slapped him on the back and patted him on the head. It was like he was a pet dog. Was he some sort of hero? I didn't get it, so I went over to Sam, who was the team captain.

"Who is that guy? Why do they call him Bengo?" I asked.

Sam winked. "You'll see, Smithy," he said.

My name is Paul Smith, but everyone calls me Smithy.

Dan, our coach, called us over.

"OK, boys," he said, clapping his hands. "Get yourselves warmed up."

We turned to jog down the touchline, but Dan called us back.

"Oh, before you go, let's give our Bengo a clap. He's been out for a while."

So everybody clapped. I clapped too, but I didn't know why. Nobody clapped me when I joined the team.

I looked at Sam. "What's all this about?" I asked.

Sam tapped his nose. "You'll see," he said again.

After all the fuss, Bengo didn't even start the game. He sat on the bench with the coach and two other boys.

It was cold – really cold. The wind was freezing and I was shivering like a leaf. I didn't want to stand around waiting for the whistle. I just wanted to get going.

"At last," I said when the ref started the game.

I took up my position in midfield and got the ball right away. Our opponents in the North City Under-13s were St Andrew's Jaguars, the Jags. The Jags was better than our nickname. Our team was called LMN Juniors. LMN was a stupid name and everybody called us the Lemons.

I tried to spray the ball out to the right, but it spun out of play.

"See! That's why you're called the Lemons," said one of the nearest Jags' player with a snort.

That hurt. I had to put things right. When that kid who'd laughed at us got the ball, I went in with a strong tackle. He fell and started rolling around like they do on the TV. He even beat the ground with his fist.

"Get up," I told him. "I hardly touched you."

The ref wagged his finger. "That was a tackle from behind, son," he said to me. "I don't want any more of that."

"I hardly touched him!" I protested.

"It was a rash tackle," the ref said.

There was no point arguing with the ref. I knew the Jags player had made too much of my tackle, but I nodded and went to help him get up.

The Jags kid scowled at me. "Not just lemons," he said. "Dirty lemons."

This was turning into a bit of a bad-tempered match.

Soon after, I got the ball again. This time I didn't waste it. Ameer was calling for the ball, so I hit it long but low, right to his feet. He volleyed it first time and it cracked against the post.

"Close," I shouted.

Ameer nodded to me. "Give me more passes like that," he said.

I gave him the thumbs up and the kid I had tackled gave me an evil look.

"You couldn't pass like that again," he said.

"Oh, shut up, Mr Grumpy," I said.

Our captain, Sam, who was nearby, heard what I'd said and laughed. "Mr Grumpy," he said. "Suits him."

Grumpy didn't like his new nickname and it got him all riled up.

I was so busy laughing with Sam that I took my eye off the match. Suddenly, there was a

shout from another of my team-mates. "Smithy!
Wake up, Smithy!"

"Close him down," someone else called.

Grumpy was racing towards me with the
ball at his feet. I did a sliding tackle, but he
skipped over it, sprinted past me and crossed
the ball from the edge of the box. I rolled onto

my stomach just in time to see the ball fly into the back of the net.

"Goal!"

Everybody stared at me. We were 1–0 down and it was my fault.

"Sorry," I said.

Ameer shook his head. "We should call you Dreamer," he told me.

Grumpy was loving it. "I've got you in my pocket," he said to me.

I jumped to my feet and squared up to him. "Think so, do you? We'll see."

But he was right. He was as quick as lightning and just before half-time he beat me again. He went past me as if I wasn't there, burst into the penalty area and fired the ball into the roof of the net.

As Grumpy walked back to the halfway line, he was grinning from ear to ear. "What's the score, Dreamer?"

He made the numbers in the air with his fingers. I tried to think of something clever to say, but I had nothing. No comeback at all.

*

At half-time, Dan called us together.

"Sorry, Smithy," he said. "It's not working, is it? We need to do something to stop them. Sam, you play in Smithy's position."

He was taking me off. I felt rubbish.

"Bengo, you're coming on. No defensive duties. Just make runs towards their goal. We need to get back into this game."

At least now I was on the subs' bench I had a chance to see what Bengo could do and what all the fuss was about.

It didn't take long. Sam kicked the ball all the way across the field soon after the restart. Bengo took it down with one touch and set off down the wing. He was even quicker than

Grumpy. The Jags full-back only just got Bengo's cross off the line.

"This Bengo kid is quick," I said out loud.

"The quickest," Dan said. "Best player I have ever managed."

"So why didn't you play him from the start?" I asked.

But Dan was too busy watching the match to answer.

*

We kept pressing, but we just couldn't put the ball in the net. With ten minutes to go, Bengo set off on another of his runs. This time he put in a perfect cross. Ameer nodded it in from close range. The score was 2–1. We had the chance to draw level. There was still time.

I shouted over to Grumpy. "You're not smiling now," I said.

Bengo wasn't finished. Right on full-time, he beat his man to the ball, turned and hit the ball low and hard into the penalty area. Ameer was in again, hitting it home from close range.

2–2.

The whistle went a minute later. It had been hard work, but we'd finished the match with a draw.

Sam put his arm round Bengo. "Well in, Bengo!" he said. "Bengo, super sub."

I had to admit it was true – Bengo *was* a super sub. But if he was such a good player, why had Dan left him on the subs' bench for so long? And I still didn't know why they called him Bengo.

HISTORICAL SUBSTITUTES

A substitute is a player who comes on to the pitch to replace another player. Maybe the first player has been injured or is tired, or maybe they aren't playing their best. The substitute is sent on to play instead. Today, teams plan who their substitutes are going to be ahead of the game. But when substitutes were first used in football matches, it was more of an informal fix at the last minute.

Early substitutions

The first records of substitutes are in match reports from the 1850s and 1860s. If a player didn't turn up for a game, then a substitute was used. They were sometimes called "emergencies".

The first substitute in international football was sent on to the pitch on 15 April 1889. Wales were playing Scotland. The Welsh goalkeeper Jim Trainer didn't turn up. A local amateur player, Alf Pugh, took his place at the start of the match. He played for twenty minutes until a substitute, Sam Gillam, arrived at the ground to replace him.

A dangerous position

But substitutions were not officially allowed in professional football until the second half of the twentieth century. Up until then, if one of your players got injured, there was nothing you could do. And in some cases this meant that players stayed on the pitch and tried to play on when it was dangerous for them to do so.

Bert Trautmann, for example, broke his neck in a collision in the FA Cup final in 1956 but somehow managed to stay on the pitch. Trautmann even saved another goal and his team, Manchester City, won the match. Luckily, Trautmann made a full recovery.

Chapter 2
The break

We had a training session the next Thursday. It was cold and misty when I arrived and there was nobody around.

"Is anybody there?" I asked.

The fog made spooky shapes around the sports centre. I was peering through one of the windows when a hand fell on my shoulder. It was the caretaker. I jumped with fright.

"Are you here for Under-13 training?" he asked.

My heart was still banging, but I nodded a yes.

"One of your mates is round the other side," he said.

Guess who? It was our super sub from the match on Sunday. He was hopping from one foot to the other.

"So why do they call you Bengo?" I asked.

Bengo grinned. "Well, I'm fast, aren't I?" he said.

"Yes," I agreed, "very fast."

"So," Bengo said, "the first time the guys saw how fast I was, I beat a defender for pace and guess what they shouted?"

I gave a shrug. "I don't know," I said.

Bengo laughed. "Go, Ben, go. See? Bengo!"

Now I got it.

"Grumpy skinned you on Sunday, didn't he?" Bengo said.

I could feel my face turning red.

"We can work on some things," he said. "Don't get upset just because you had a bad game. Learn from your mistakes and come back stronger."

"How do I do that?" I asked. "That kid turned me inside out."

"I'll show you a few tricks," he said.

We were still the only ones there, so we picked up a ball and went out on the field. Bengo put himself in charge.

"Turn your body before I get to you," Bengo said. "You need to force me out wide so you can get a tackle in or deny me space."

On the third attempt, I got the ball off him.
"Yes!" I shouted, punching the air.

That's when we heard Dan.

"Good to see you getting to know each other," he said.

"Sorry I messed up on Sunday," I said, looking down at the ground.

"One poor game doesn't make you a bad player," Dan said. "We'll work on it."

"We've already started," Bengo said.

Dan smiled. "So I see."

By then the other boys were arriving. Soon Dan had us working on our passing, then we practised a few set-pieces.

Bengo wasn't just quick. He was brilliant at corners and free kicks. He was even better at penalties. He was ice cool. He didn't get nervous at all. He scored the first six on the run. Even when he missed the seventh, it didn't bother him. He scored the next three.

"Nine out of ten," he said. "Not bad."

"Not bad?" I said. "That's fantastic. I wish I was that good. Why didn't you start the season with the rest of us?"

"Don't you know the story?"

"Story?" I said. "What story?"

Bengo didn't look as if he wanted to tell me, but he explained. "It happened at the end of last season," he began. "With four games to go, I was playing out on the wing, but I was still top scorer."

"Tell Smithy about the scout," Sam said.

Bengo nodded. "The youth scout from City came down to see me play. I thought I was going to get on their books. I've always wanted to be a professional footballer."

"So what went wrong?"

"I had the beating of this full-back."

Sam grinned. "A bit like the way Grumpy had you in his pocket, Smithy."

I gave him a dig in the ribs. "Shut up," I said. "I want to hear Bengo's story."

Bengo carried on. "The boy was getting really fed up, so he lunged at me. He crunched into my ankle. I knew it was broken right away."

All I could say was, "Ouch."

"It was in plaster for six weeks," Bengo said, "but it didn't get better. The doctor had to reset it."

"That's rotten," I said. "Just when you thought you'd hit the big time."

"Yes," Bengo said. "It's been hard."

But he was back now and he was playing so well that next time the scouts would definitely spot him. So what was the problem?

"Cheer up," I said. "You were brilliant on Sunday, man of the match. Without you, we'd have lost good style."

We were still talking when Dan called us all together.

"OK, boys," he said. "I bet you want to know the team for Sunday."

I had a good idea what he was going to say.

"I'm going with the team that finished the game last week," he said. "Sorry, Smithy. You'll be on the bench."

I'd been taken off in the last match, so I wasn't surprised, but I was still gutted.

My eyes were stinging, but I wasn't going to cry in front of the others. I just drifted off to one side.

Bengo came over. "Are you OK?" he asked.

"I'm fine."

"Don't just take it," he said. "We can practise together. How's that?"

I shrugged, but he wasn't taking no for an answer and shoved me.

"I said, how's that?" he asked.

"Thanks," I said. "That will be great. I'm going to get my place back."

Bengo winked. "Of course you are," he said.

A NEED FOR CHANGE

These days we are used to seeing substitutes on the sidelines of a match – they sit on the bench, waiting to be put into play. That wasn't how it used to be. For a long time, subs weren't allowed at all in professional football. If a player was injured, they would have to play on, like Bert Trautmann, or their team would have to carry on without them. If a player was forced to go off the pitch and their team was left with only ten men, the other side had a big advantage.

An unfair advantage

In the 1959 FA Cup final, Roy Dwight gave Nottingham Forest the lead against Luton Town. But when the team were up 2–0, Dwight broke his leg. There was still an hour of the match to go. Forest only just hung on with ten men to win 2–1.

Blackburn Rovers were not so lucky the next year. Their full-back Dave Whelan broke his leg just before half-time. This time the injury decided the match. With only ten men on the pitch, Blackburn lost 0–3 to

Wolves. And Whelan's injury meant he couldn't play football again.

It was injuries like these that made the people in charge of football in England change the rules.

Change is coming

In-game substitutions were introduced in the qualifying rounds of the 1954 World Cup. The first substitute was Richard Gottinger, who came on to replace Horst Eckel for West Germany in a 3–0 win over Saarland in 1953. West Germany went on to win the tournament in 1954, but Gottinger never played for his country again.

Many other countries changed their rules during this decade to allow the use of substitutes, but it didn't happen in the UK until 1965.

Chapter 3
Bottling it

"Look at him go," I said to Kingsley, one of the other subs who was sitting on the bench with me the next Sunday.

Kingsley nodded, then shouted, "Go, Ben, go!"

Bengo was really something. I watched him turn his marker inside out, jinking this way and that. He went left, went right, then he dropped his shoulder. The full-back tried to turn but was left sprawled on the ground.

"See that?" Kingsley said.

"He's got it all: speed, strength, skill," I said, and looked at Dan. "What do you think, boss?"

Dan nodded. Somehow, I expected him to be more positive about Bengo. Was I missing something?

Bengo only had the keeper to beat. He was about to pull the trigger, but the keeper was rushing forward. Bengo stopped dead. The keeper saw his chance and cleared the ball upfield.

"What just happened?" I said. "I thought that was going to be a goal for sure."

Dan shrugged, but he knew something. I could see it in his face.

"Bengo," Kingsley shouted, "what happened, bro?"

Bengo just turned and jogged back downfield. He didn't look happy. Not one bit.

"I don't get it," I said. "He could have beaten the keeper to the ball. Easy."

"But he didn't, did he?" Kingsley said. "He bottled it."

*

It wasn't the only time it happened during that match. We were playing North Bank Under-13s. They weren't as good as the Jags the week before. But they made up for their lack of skill by going after our best players like a pack of dogs. Some of the tackles were bang out of order. Their centre-back brought Ameer down just before half-time. Ameer never faked it. The tackle had knocked the wind out of him.

"Come on, ref," Kingsley shouted. "That was a rugby tackle."

Sam came over to Dan. "Have a word, coach," he said. "We're getting no protection."

Dan nodded. "I'll talk to the ref at half-time."

*

The first half ended 0–0 and we saw Dan approach the ref. Bengo stood on his own, staring at the ground.

"Are you OK?" I asked.

"I'm fine," Bengo answered.

But he wasn't.

Dan finished talking to the ref.

"Coach," I said, "what's the matter with Bengo?"

Dan shrugged, but Sam let me in on the secret.

"Keep it to yourself, Smithy," he said, "but Bengo played in a couple of pre-season matches – games to get himself fit. He played some great stuff, but every time there was the chance of a physical challenge, he pulled out."

I glanced at Bengo. He looked as if he was feeling sorry for himself.

"I heard Dan talking about it to one of the other coaches. He said it was hard work getting Bengo to play again. That's why he started the season late. The problem isn't physical. It's in his head."

"What do we do?" I asked

Sam shook his head. "I'm not sure. I've tried to get him to talk about it, but he doesn't want to know. You and Bengo seem to get along well. Maybe you can get through to him."

"I'll try," I told him.

*

It was the same story in the second half. Bengo was on fire. He even set up the first goal. He came deep, picked up the ball and set off down the touchline. He tempted the full-back out, then beat him for pace and left him way behind.

Kingsley took up his war cry: "Go, Ben, go!"

Bengo fired in a low cross and Ameer volleyed it into the net.

1–0.

That was as good as it got. North Bank had been on the back foot for two thirds of the match. Then they got a corner. Their winger swung it in and Sam lost his man. It was an easy nod in by their striker.

"Were you fast asleep there, Sam?" Ameer shouted. "We should be 3– or 4–0 up and now it's 1–1."

Sam looked down. "Sorry," he said.

Bengo was keen to put us back in the lead. From the kick-off he headed downfield. Bengo was already on the edge of the area when the full-back tried to close him down. As the full-back got near, Bengo went down in a heap.

Dan frowned. He ran over to Bengo. "Are you all right, son?" he asked.

"I never touched him!" the full-back protested. "Honest, I never."

Bengo stood up. "He's right," he said. "I slipped."

It was half true. We all knew he went down so as to get out of the way of the tackle. He had bottled it again.

"I'm making a change," Dan told the ref. "Go and have a rest, Bengo." He was more sad than angry. "Smithy, you're on."

Bengo trooped off and pulled on his jacket. He looked really upset.

It was up to me to use the skills I'd been practising with Bengo. Just before full-time, we got a corner. I looked over at Dan. He nodded. "Go for it, son."

When the corner came in, I threw myself at the ball. I didn't get it right. The ball smacked me in the face. It stung like mad. I was still rubbing the mud out of my eyes when I felt everybody crowding round.

"What are you doing?" I asked.

"We got a goal, you muppet," Ameer laughed. "You scored!"

"It hit me in the face," I said.

"Yes," said Ameer, "and flew in off your nose."

I touched my nose. "I've got a nosebleed," I said, looking at my fingers.

"Who cares?" one of the other boys said. "It doesn't matter how you scored. We won!"

*

After the match, I walked to the road with Bengo.

"How's the nose?" Bengo asked.

"Fine," I told him.

Maybe this was a good time to talk.

"You're scared of getting injured, aren't you?" I said to him.

Bengo looked back at me.

"That lad didn't touch you, did he?" I asked.

Bengo looked away. "You don't know what you're talking about."

Then he pointed out a black four-by-four. "That's my dad," he said. "I'll see you later."

NEW RULES

The English Football League first allowed substitutes during the 1965–66 season. For the first two seasons after the change to the rules, each side was only allowed one substitution for injury during a game.

The first substitute and the first goal

Keith Peacock was the first substitute in the English game. His big moment for Charlton Athletic arrived on 21 August 1965 when goalkeeper Mike Rose was injured eleven minutes into their match against Bolton Wanderers and Peacock went on to play. But he didn't play in goal – another player took the keeper's place. Peacock played more than 500 times for Charlton Athletic but is remembered best for that game in 1965 when he was sent on as a substitute.

Slightly later on that same day in August 1965, Bobby Knox also took to the pitch as a substitute – for Barrow AFC against Wrexham. He became the first ever player to score a goal after coming on as a substitute and Barrow won the game 2–1.

Scotland follows suit

Archie Gemmill was the first substitute in the Scottish game. He came on for St Mirren in a League Cup tie against Clyde on 13 August 1966 to replace Jim Clunie. Later that month, Paul Conn became the first official substitute in a Scottish League match when he came on for Queen's Park in a match against Albion Rovers.

More subs, please

In the 1967–68 season, the rule was changed to allow substitutions for tactical reasons as well as for injury. In 1987–88, two substitutes were allowed, which rose to three in the 1990s. During the COVID pandemic in 2020, a temporary rule was introduced to allow the use of five substitutes.

Chapter 4
Part of the game

Somebody was missing at training the week after our match with North Bank.

"Has anybody seen Bengo?" Dan asked.

Everybody shrugged.

"What about you, Smithy?" Dan asked hopefully. "Have you heard from him?"

"Not a word," I said.

I didn't tell him I'd been messaging Bengo every day. He hadn't replied.

"Well, if you hear from him, let me know," Dan said.

I nodded. I couldn't stop thinking about Bengo for the whole of the training session. How could somebody as good as he was give up like this? I needed to do something about it. While Dan was putting the balls away, I asked if anybody knew Bengo's address.

"Yes, he lives on Stone Street," Sam said.

"What number?" I asked him.

Sam didn't know.

"But you can't miss it," Sam said. "It's the second house as you turn off Broadway. It's got a red door."

Ameer was banging his boots against the wall to get the mud off. "Are you going to see him?" he asked.

I nodded. "Somebody needs to talk to him," I said.

So off I went. Sam's directions were spot on. I saw the house with the red door right away and knocked.

Bengo came to the door and frowned. "Did Dan send you?" he asked.

"No," I told him. "It was all my idea. I've been messaging you."

Bengo nodded. "Yes, I saw the messages. Look, I'm not sure I want to go on playing for the team."

"You can't just give up," I said. "You're the best winger I've ever seen."

Bengo stopped me. "I'm the best *player* you've ever seen," he said.

It was hard to argue.

"OK," I said. "So you're the best player I've ever seen. You could get on the books of a professional team. Why throw it all away?

Nobody wants to get injured, but it's part of the game."

"Easy for you to say," Bengo grunted. "You've never broken a bone. Look, I don't mean to bottle it. It's just ... when it comes to a fifty-fifty ball, I pull out of the tackle."

"You'll get over it," I said.

Bengo dug his hands in his pockets. "Are you sure about that?" he said.

"You can at least give it a go," I said. "Come along on Sunday."

Bengo didn't seem sure, but at least he didn't say no. "I'll think about it," he said.

*

Our next match was with Red Lion Rangers. I got a start against them. So did Kingsley. But a few minutes to go before kick-off, there was still no sign of Bengo.

Rangers were bottom of the table and it was easy to see why. Right from the start, they had no belief in themselves. We were beating them easily. Ameer scored the first goal after just five minutes. Then Kingsley got a goal in with a header straight from the restart.

Sam winked to me. "This could be a cricket score," he said.

*

I got on the score sheet just before half-time when I ran in to head a great corner by Kingsley. It bounced in off my chest.

"Well, at least it's not your nose this time," Sam joked.

We went in 3–0 up at half-time. I should have been over the moon, but I was fed up. Why hadn't Bengo showed up? I thought he'd agreed to give it another go.

"Never mind," Sam told me. "At least you tried."

*

In the second half, we scored twice more to run out 5–0 winners.

"That was a great win," Sam said, "and I've got some more good news, Smithy."

"What's that?" I asked.

Sam nodded towards the gate. Bengo was there with his dad. I jogged over to talk to him.

"How come you didn't show up until now?" I asked.

"I wasn't going to come at all," Bengo said. "Then I got thinking about what you said – about throwing it all away."

"So what made the difference?" I asked.

Bengo laughed. "You did."

"You're kidding?" I gasped. "I thought you didn't want to know."

"Well, I'm here, aren't I?" Bengo said.

"So you're going to give it a go?" I asked.

Bengo nodded. "Looks like it."

HOW DO MANAGERS USE SUBS TO CHANGE THE MATCH?

Tactical tricks

When substitutes were first allowed in 1965, they could only be used if a player was injured. But some managers were suspected of trying to bend the new rule. Don Revie, a famous manager of Leeds United, was one of those accused of telling players to pretend they had an injury so that a substitute could be sent on to replace them.

Getting it right

In the 1970s, Liverpool manager Bob Paisley created the first "super sub" – David Fairclough. Fairclough made 154 appearances for Liverpool over eight years, 62 of which came from the bench as a substitute. He scored 18 goals as a substitute and changed the course of many important matches.

Win or lose

Managers can win matches by making a substitution. They can also lose them. Claudio Ranieri has done both. When he was Chelsea manager in the first leg of the 2004 Champions League semi-final, he made three substitutions that many people believe led Chelsea to lose the match against Monaco 3–1.

In 2010, when he was manager of Roma, Ranieri got it right. In an important derby match against Lazio, he made two substitutions, but this time his team scored twice as a result and won the match 2–1.

Perfect timing

Fresh players can have a big effect when the rest of the team is getting tired. Experienced players can help their teams hold on to a lead. A manager might swap attackers for extra defenders when a team is trying to hold on to a lead.

It is all about bringing the right player on at the right time. Managers who get it right become heroes. Managers who get it wrong might not be in the job for long!

Chapter 5
Making a difference

We had a good result against Red Lion Rangers, but other than that we hadn't really set the world on fire this season. We'd been leaking goals in defence and we lacked pace up front. In other words, we had been missing Bengo. It left us in fifth place out of twelve teams in the league.

On the sunny Sunday afternoon of our next match, Dan called us together.

"We need to step up our game if we're going to challenge for top spot," Dan said. "Maybe the

North City Cup's a better bet than the junior league. We'll find out who we're up against in the first round after today's game."

That gave us something to look forward to. It wasn't the only boost. Bengo had arrived early, ready to play, but Dan wasn't about to rush him back into the side. He was one of the subs.

"We're up against Dinamo Hightown today. They're the best opposition we've played," Dan said. "They are top of the league and they deserve to be. They've got great team spirit and a couple of real stand-out players." He turned to me. "Smithy, you need to watch out for one of their wingers," he said.

My heart missed a beat.

"You've got to be on top of your game today," Dan went on, looking right at me. "You can't give that lad an inch of space. He's called Gary Speed. Speed by name, speed by nature."

I must have looked nervous, because Bengo came over. "Remember what we did in training," he said. "Don't let him catch you flat-footed. You've got to be on the turn as he comes at you."

I nodded. "Got you," I said, but I sounded more confident than I felt.

We were on the back foot right from the kick-off. Dinamo just kept coming forward. It was breathless stuff. Crosses kept coming in. Every time we cleared them, the ball went back to a Dinamo player.

Gary Speed had the right name. I did everything to slow him down. He didn't get past me, but he was able to put in plenty of crosses. We were lucky not to be at least a goal down.

"We can't go on like this," Sam said.

He was bent double with his hands on his knees. He was breathing heavily. I went over to the touchline to take a throw-in.

"Listen, Smithy," Bengo whispered to me from the bench. "Try to get a bit tighter on that Speed kid. Don't dive in. Just try to stick a bit closer to him."

"Easy for you to say," I told him as I took the throw-in.

But Bengo was right and I did what he said. I followed Gary Speed around as if I was his shadow and tried to put him off his game. It

worked. There weren't as many crosses and the game was more even.

"I think we've got them now," Kingsley said.

He spoke too soon. Just when things were getting better, the Dinamo centre-half punted the ball forward. Sam tried to chest it down but made a real mess of it. The ball squirted under him and the Dinamo striker had the easiest of tap-ins. We'd done all the hard stuff and now we'd let in a really easy goal. It just didn't seem fair.

"Sorry," Sam said. "I got the ball all wrong."

Dan decided to make a change at half-time. "We need to give their defence something to think about," he said. "We've done OK keeping it down to 1–0, but we need to do more than just defend."

He nodded to Bengo. "Come on, super sub. You're our secret weapon."

Bengo had been good at giving me advice, but now he looked really unsure of himself.

"Go for it," I said. "Remember – you told me what to do a while ago and it made all the difference. Take some of your own advice."

*

Dinamo started the second half the way they started the first. I had stopped the crosses coming in from the right side of the pitch, but they were getting a lot of joy down the left. It was only a matter of time before they got their second goal.

It came when Kingsley gave away a penalty. We were 2–0 down with only fifteen minutes to go.

"Come on, Bengo," I said. "We need you to show what you can do."

Bengo nodded. "Just get me a pass I can run onto," he said.

I nodded.

With ten minutes to go, it looked like Dinamo had the game in the bag. They weren't going forward as much.

I spotted Bengo making a run and punted it right to his feet. He pushed forward, beating first one defender then another. On the edge of the area, he opened up his body and put his shot past the keeper into the top right-hand corner.

"Goal!"

One piece of brilliance had put us back in the game.

"If you can do that again," Bengo told me, "we can get back on level terms. You never know, we might even win it."

Gary Speed had other ideas. He got the ball from the kick-off and made a run, but I was ready for him. I slid in, got up again fast and hit a long ball downfield. This time, Bengo didn't even take a touch. He ran onto the pass and struck it on the volley. It was a goal as soon as it left his foot.

He peeled away with his arms in the air and ran half the length of the field. None of us could

catch him. When he reached the halfway line, he did a couple of somersaults.

"Show-off!" I said when I caught up with him.

He laughed. "You're only jealous," he said.

The game ended 2–2. Another draw. But Bengo had changed everything.

"You're becoming the draw experts," Dan said. "But do you want to hear who you're playing against in the Cup?"

We told him to give us the news.

"It's the Jags," Dan said. "A grudge match, eh?"

"Are you up for that one?" Bengo asked me.

I nodded, but I wasn't sure.

SUPER SUBS!

The subs listed below have all come on at key points in a match and changed the outcome.

Ole Gunnar Solskjaer

Manchester United's Ole Gunnar Solskjaer was nicknamed the "baby-faced assassin". The Norwegian was the greatest super sub of all time. He scored 126 goals in 366 games for the club, 28 of which he scored as a substitute.

His most famous super-sub goal was in the 1999 Champions League final against Bayern Munich. He came on in the 81st minute and scored in injury time. This victory meant Manchester United won the Premier League, FA Cup and Champions League treble.

Henrik Larsson

Henrik Larsson was nicknamed "King of Kings" when he played for Celtic. When he joined Barcelona in 2004, they won two league titles and the Champions League. In the 2006 Champions League final he came on after an hour and set up goals for Samuel Eto'o and

Juliano Belletti to give Barcelona a 2–1 victory over Arsenal.

David Trezeguet

David Trezeguet came off the bench many times for Juventus and other clubs. He was also a super sub for France. During the UEFA European Championship final in 2000, Trezeguet came on towards the end of the game and scored in extra time to give France their victory over Italy. It was a real golden goal.

Tim Cahill

Tim Cahill was Australia's super sub. He came on in their first 2006 World Cup match against Japan with 20 minutes to go. The Socceroos were losing by a single goal and Cahill scored twice. It was Australia's first ever winning match in the World Cup. Cahill did the same job at Everton when the Toffees needed him. Whenever he scored a goal, he would pretend to have a punch-up with the corner flag!

Chapter 6
Super sub

Dan was giving us his team talk the next Sunday. We were kicking off against the Jags in the Cup in just ten minutes.

"It's time we stopped drawing and started winning," he said. "We're still dropping points. We're defending better, but we keep making daft mistakes."

Sam went red. He couldn't forget how he'd lost his man in the game against Dinamo Hightown.

"Keep your mind on the match, boys," Dan said. "You're all good players, but you need to come together as a team. Someone has to take charge and organise you when you're on the pitch."

He meant Sam.

"And we need to toughen up."

He meant Bengo.

But there was a surprise when Dan announced the team. Super sub wasn't even in the starting eleven. Our best player – and he was only a sub!

I nudged Bengo. "How can he leave you out after last Sunday?" I said. "Without you, we would never have got that draw. It was you that got us back in the game."

"I got some help from you," Bengo said. "It's OK playing well in short bursts. Dan still doesn't

know how I'll cope when the going gets tough."
Then he pulled a face, remembering the times
he had pulled out of tackles. "And I don't know
either."

We lined up for kick-off and there was my
old rival Grumpy doing a few stretches. Thanks
to Bengo, I was ready for him this time. He
wasn't going to make a fool out of me today.
Bengo had shown me how to improve my game.

"Are you ready for another football lesson?"
Grumpy said.

I was nervous, but I tried to look confident.
"In your dreams," I told him.

We all wanted to defend better this time
and we did. Grumpy was making runs, but I
kept forcing him out wide. I didn't give him any
room at all. He just ran out of space in the end
and couldn't get his cross in. Grumpy frowned.
He couldn't understand why he wasn't doing
better against me.

Sam was playing better in central defence,
barking out orders. We were defending better
all round, but we weren't scoring any goals. Just
before half-time, I could see that Grumpy was
breathing heavily. He started drifting into the
middle of the pitch.

"What's wrong?" I asked. "Aren't you getting any joy on the wing?"

He didn't like that, but he couldn't think of a reply.

We played out the first half with neither side scoring any goals.

"That was much better in defence," Dan said when we ran in at half-time, "but we're not giving Ameer any support up front. I think it's time to bring on Bengo. Are you ready, super sub?"

I still didn't understand why Bengo hadn't started the game. Maybe Dan still had doubts about him.

Bengo nodded, but he didn't say anything. He still didn't seem too sure of himself.

*

In the second half, we slipped into our old bad habits. Grumpy had dropped back into midfield and he spotted that we weren't marking the Jags' full-back on the edge of the area. He put in a perfect pass and we were a goal down.

"That was just careless!" Dan shouted. "You can't leave a man free like that."

We tightened up, but we still weren't getting the ball to Bengo or Ameer. I thought I'd try to get forward a bit more. There was a risk. It might give Grumpy more space to make runs, but we had to score.

Halfway through the second half, I saw my chance. Grumpy was meant to mark me when I went forward, but he was more interested in going for a second goal. He wasn't doing his defensive job.

I set off on a run. Bengo raced into the area, ready for my pass.

The Jags centre-half had other ideas. He crunched into a tackle and Bengo went down with a loud cry. Things looked bad. This was the end of Bengo's match for sure.

"Ref, that was out of order," Sam complained. "He went for the man, not the ball."

Bengo lay still for a moment. Was he going to get up?

"Are you OK?" I asked as I ran over to him.

I looked over at Dan. I was sure he'd take Bengo off the pitch.

Then we all got the surprise of our lives. Bengo was back on his feet and yelling at the centre-half. His eyes were hard and his fists were clenched. He wasn't limping off the pitch; he was angry. I had to hold him back.

"What kind of tackle do you call that?" Bengo shouted.

The lad who tackled him was backing off.
He held his hands up. "Sorry," the boy said.
"I got the timing wrong."

Bengo walked away, shaking his head.
"Yeah, sure you did," he said with a grunt.

Sam gave me a nudge. "Bengo stayed on the
field," he said. "That's got to be good."

I glanced at Bengo. He still looked pumped up.

"This is the Bengo we need," I said. "Tough and angry."

*

Five minutes later, Grumpy was back infield again. He wasn't marking me and I was free. I set off down the wing and passed to Bengo. The full-back marking him tried to get in a tackle, but Bengo beat him for pace, then he put the ball on a plate for Ameer. Ameer smashed it into the roof of the net.

1–1.

We were back in the match.

"That tackle didn't bother you then?" I asked Bengo.

"They all bother me," Bengo said, "but I've got to get over it or give up, and I'm not giving up."

"Go, Ben, go," shouted Sam.

After that, the match was end-to-end stuff. Both teams were hunting after the winner. Grumpy had one more go at beating me, but nobody was getting past me that morning.

I took the ball off him, looked up and saw that Bengo was free. He was like a ghost, drifting into gaps in the Jags defence.

I fired the ball downfield and Bengo picked it up perfectly, hurdling one tackle, then stumbling over another. He seemed off balance, but the tackles weren't stopping him. He shoved his marker to one side and managed to toe-poke the ball into the area. It rolled behind Ameer, but Kingsley came in and swept the ball into the net.

2–1.

We threw ourselves on Bengo and Kingsley. Suddenly, they were the perfect partnership. Then it was all hands to the pumps as the Jags tried to find an equaliser. We hadn't won yet and they were no pushover

"Hold on, lads," Sam said, clapping his hands. "We've got to keep them out."

"Good to see our captain getting a grip," Dan said from the touchline.

It was attack after attack by the Jags. There was some desperate defending. Then, with a minute to go, Grumpy found some space. He burst into the area and was about to pull the trigger when a tackle came in from a defender no one had seen.

Bengo.

Grumpy went down in the area. For a moment everyone held their breath. Was the

ref going to whistle for a penalty? Then the ref
put his arms in the air. It was a clean tackle.

There wasn't time for another attack. The
whistle went. 2–1. We'd done it! We were
through to the next round.

All the boys went wild and there was no doubt about the man of the match. Bengo had two assists to his name and a match-saving tackle.

*

When the celebrations were finally over, we walked home together, me and Bengo.

"You finally got over your injury," I said.

"I had to at some point," Bengo said.

I laughed.

"I expected you to set up the goals," I told him, "but I didn't see that one coming – Bengo putting in the perfect tackle to stop them scoring."

"Me neither," Bengo said. "If I hadn't got in the tackle, they would have equalised."

"But you did it," I said. "You won that match. Well in, super sub."

Our books are tested
for children and young people by
children and young people.

Thanks to everyone who consulted on
a manuscript for their time and effort in
helping us to make our books better
for our readers.